Leo Politi

April 14-1966

# PICCOLO'S PRANK

## LEO POLITI

CHARLES SCRIBNER'S SONS
NEW YORK

to Rose
who loved and took
care of the birds and
little animals
on Bunker Hill

IN the center of the city of Los Angeles there is a cable car railway called Angel's Flight that runs to the top of Bunker Hill.

On Bunker Hill lived Luigi and his tiny monkey Piccolo. Piccolo in Italian means "little one."

Early every morning Luigi and Piccolo went to the park to perform for people.

Sometimes Piccolo was dressed as a clown and sometimes he wore a Mexican costume with a very large straw hat. In his hat Piccolo looked like a huge mushroom.

Luigi made Piccolo a little pair of skates. Everyone liked the monkey's skating act best of all. As Luigi played his organ, Piccolo skipped, hopped and twirled. Some-

times he slipped and fell, making everyone laugh and laugh. Then Piccolo bowed and tipped his hat, and the people gave him pennies.

When they finished their performance in the park, Luigi bought a bag of peanuts from the peanut man. Piccolo ate them on the way home.

Piccolo always looked forward to the cable car ride up Angel's Flight. When the little trolley began to climb the steep hill, his eyes grew wide with wonder. The crowds on the street looked smaller and smaller. As the cable car climbed higher and higher, Luigi and Piccolo could see the whole city spread out before them.

When they reached the top, Luigi handed Piccolo a nickel. Piccolo gave the money to the conductor to pay for their fare.

Strolling home through the narrow streets of Bunker Hill, Luigi and Piccolo passed many old houses. People called them gingerbread houses because they were decorated with carved ornaments. Trees and flowers grew in the gardens. Morning glories climbed everywhere. They seemed to like the old houses.

As Luigi went by the homes of friends, he called out greetings. Rose was in her garden, feeding the pigeons. "Good afternoon, Luigi and Piccolo," she said.

Luigi bowed and tipped his hat. Piccolo bowed and tipped *his* hat.

Next door lived an old man. Because he had a long white beard the children called him Santa Claus. Further down the road lived Madame Dornfell who had once been a famous opera singer. She kept a pet parrot and taught him to sing beautiful arias.

Luigi and his monkey lived in a large pink house
with a tower.

Four children, who also lived on the hill, came
running when they saw Piccolo.

"Piccolo is home, Piccolo is home," they shouted.
Ruby, Julie, Billy and Susie were Piccolo's best friends.
Every day they waited to play with him.

They liked to watch him climb trees and swing from one branch to the other.

They held their breath when Piccolo scrambled across the roof of Luigi's house and perched on the very top of the tower. The tower was so high that from there Piccolo could see the whole city of Los Angeles.

One day the children invited Piccolo to play at their grandmother's house at the end of the street. Mrs. Bosco lived in an interesting old gingerbread house. The children began to play hide-and-seek on the stairs and balconies. They were having so much fun they forgot about Piccolo.

All at once Billy remembered the monkey. "Where is Piccolo?" he asked. The children searched everywhere but they could not find him. They ran to Luigi crying, "Piccolo is lost."

Luigi knew his pet very well. "Don't be upset," he said. "I know where to find him."

Luigi led the children to an old abandoned car parked across the street. He bent down and said, "Piccolo, come out of there."

A minute later out crawled Piccolo, covered with grease and oil. Luigi was not pleased. "You are a bad monkey," he scolded.

The children laughed because Piccolo looked so funny. "Piccolo," Julie said, "you are a *mechanic* monkey."

The next day, coming home from the park, Piccolo was friskier than usual. He hopped on Luigi's left shoulder as the cable car climbed Bunker Hill. Then he hopped on Luigi's right shoulder.

Suddenly he hopped to the window and leaped out. Luigi looked out the window and saw Piccolo crawl under the cable car.

"Stop! Stop!" shrieked a woman in a flowered hat. "The monkey is trapped."

Luigi tugged the emergency cord. At once the conductor pulled a lever. The cable car came to a halt.

Passengers looked out the windows and shouted to people on the street. People on the street looked up at the cable car on Angel's Flight and shouted to the passengers.

"Everyone stay calm," said the conductor firmly.
"I will call the fire department." He pressed an alarm
button.

Within minutes Luigi and the other passengers
heard sirens. The fire engines were on the way. "Hurry,
please hurry," Luigi whispered.

Soon firemen were swarming at the bottom of Angel's Flight. They cranked a wheel. A tall ladder rose up and up until it reached the cable car.

Then one brave fireman climbed to the top of the long, swaying ladder. He leaned under the trolley and brought out Piccolo, frightened but safe.

The passengers cheered. The crowds waved and shouted. Everyone was happy because Piccolo was safe. Luigi was happiest of all. He held Piccolo close to him and thanked the fireman who had rescued his pet.

As the car began to move up Angel's Flight again, Luigi zipped Piccolo into his coat pocket. Only Piccolo's head showed.

At the top of Bunker Hill, Ruby, Julie, Billy and Susie were waiting for Piccolo.

"We are so glad he is not hurt," they said when they heard about Piccolo's prank.

"I am, too," agreed Luigi. "But I am not going to take any more chances. From now on, when we ride up Angel's Flight, Piccolo will sit in my pocket."

As they walked home, the children held Piccolo's paws tightly. They knew how sad they would feel if anything ever happened to him.

And from that day on, when Luigi and Piccolo rode up Angel's Flight, Piccolo always traveled in Luigi's pocket.